Prayer
Journal
for Lent

This journal belongs to:

_____

_____

_____

Prayer Journal
for Lent

A Hayseed Journal

Hayseed Publishing, LLC
Newmarket, New Hampshire

Published by Hayseed Publishing, LLC
Post Office Box 217, Newmarket, New Hampshire 03857

ISBN: 978-1-954923-00-3

FIRST EDITION

For all of the angels in our lives

Introduction

How to Use this Journal

Thank you for taking the step of purchasing this journal and embarking on a Lenten journey to increase your faith and deepen your connection to God and the ultimate sacrifice He made for us.

Lent begins with the reminder that we are dust and to dust we shall return. Not exactly cheerful. However, this reminder cements in us the understanding that God's law is the only truth and the only way to peace, understanding and salvation. We know God's most important law is the law rooted in Jesus's command to love God with all our heart and our neighbors as ourselves. God's love and our expression of that love to God and to others is our only hope. That love is the force behind every good thing we have, experience, create or give to the world. Whatever fruit we bear comes from it rather than our own strength, wit, toil or goodness. That is what the reminder that we are dust is about and leads us to introspection and action throughout the season of Lent.

During Lent, we focus on prayer, fasting and almsgiving, which can be described as follows:

Prayer: Direct Communication with God, which can be either petitionary, in gratitude or in worship. This journal helps to focus you on each type of prayer and assists you in increasing and making the most of your prayer time.

Fasting: Denying ourselves some earthly pleasure in order to increase our spiritual focus. Fasting must have both elements of sacrifice **and** spiritual growth - otherwise, it is not fasting, it's just a diet or life goal. This journal will help you identify the areas in your life where sacrifice will bear the fruit of a deeper connection to God and His will for you.

Almsgiving: Sharing the gifts God has given us with His creation. Almsgiving is most effective when done in accordance with God's will. This journal will help you hear that still small voice directing you to give where God needs you, your time, and your treasure the most.

These practices help us understand God's law of love and help us achieve the goal of becoming more like Christ and less attached to the dusty, corporeal world in which we live. This journal is structured to help you experience Lent to its fullest. Lent should be both contemplative and active. This journal is a tool to guide your contemplative time while setting action items to ensure your Lent incorporates prayer, fasting, and almsgiving and is far deeper than those 40 days when we gave up (or tried to give up) candy as children. The journal is set up in a flexible manner allowing you to move at your own pace, reflecting and setting goals on a daily, weekly or seasonal basis. The work you do as you use this journal will help you maximize your access to and understanding of the promises God has made to us through the salvific season of Lent.

Those promises tell us that when we separate from the corporeal world and leave the dust behind, we have a chance to live in eternity with the Lord. Thank you for using this journal as you wait to experience the gift of Jesus' salvation in the Easter season. We pray this Lent brings you closer to God and deepens your alignment with his purpose for your life.

For dust you are and to dust you will return.

GENESIS 3:19

My prayer for today

_____

_____

_____

_____

_____

_____

_____

Lord, help me reach my goals for today.

In my Easter journey, I determine what is unnecessary.

Today I am conscious of the following unnecessary demands on my time:

_____

_____

_____

_____

_____

May the gifting of the Spirit flow through me to illuminate all I come into contact with today.

What gifts am I consciously giving today?

_____

_____

_____

_____

_____

Whoever dwells in the shelter of the Most High
will rest in the shadow of the Almighty.

I will say of the Lord, "He is my refuge and my fortress,
my God, in whom I trust."

PSALM 91:1-2

Lord, my refuge, hear my prayer today

_____

_____

_____

_____

_____

_____

_____

_____

Refrain

Something I can do
without today

_____

_____

_____

_____

_____

_____

_____

_____

_____

Give

Something I can give
today

_____

_____

_____

_____

_____

_____

_____

_____

_____

Gratitude

So then, just as you received Christ Jesus as Lord, continue to live your lives in him, rooted and built up in him, strengthened in the faith as you were taught, and overflowing with thankfulness.

COLOSSIANS 2:6-7

My prayer of thanksgiving

_____

_____

_____

_____

_____

_____

_____

_____

_____

_____

_____

*"Wake up, sleeper,
rise from the dead,
and Christ will shine on you."*

EPHESIANS 5:14

My prayer for today

_____
_____
_____
_____
_____
_____
_____
_____
_____

Lord, help me reach my goals for today.

In my Easter journey, I determine what is unnecessary.

Today I am conscious of the following unnecessary demands on my time:

_____

_____

_____

_____

_____

May the gifting of the Spirit flow through me to illuminate all I come into contact with today.

What gifts am I consciously giving today?

_____

_____

_____

_____

_____

But when you give to the needy, do not let your left hand know what your right hand is doing, so that your giving may be in secret. Then your Father, who sees what is done in secret, will reward you.

MATTHEW 6:3-4

Lord, hear my prayer today

_____

_____

_____

_____

_____

_____

_____

_____

_____

Refrain

Something I can do without today

_____

_____

_____

_____

_____

_____

_____

_____

_____

Give

Something I can give today

_____

_____

_____

_____

_____

_____

_____

_____

_____

Gratitude

*For everything God created is good, and nothing is to be
rejected if it is to be received with thanksgiving,
because it is consecrated by the word of God and prayer.*

1 TIMOTHY 4:4-5

My prayer of thanksgiving

_____

_____

_____

_____

_____

_____

_____

_____

_____

_____

I will not forget you!
See, I have engraved you on the palms of my hands.

ISAIAH 49:15-16

My prayer for today

_____
_____
_____
_____
_____
_____
_____
_____
_____

Lord, help me reach my goals for today.

In my Easter journey, I determine what is unnecessary.

Today I am conscious of the following unnecessary demands on my time:

_____

_____

_____

_____

_____

May the gifting of the Spirit flow through me to illuminate all I come into contact with today.

What gifts am I consciously giving today?

_____

_____

_____

_____

_____

Remember this: Whoever sows sparingly will also reap sparingly, and whoever sows generously will also reap generously. Each of you should give what you have decided in your heart to give, not reluctatly or under compulsion, for God loves a cheerful giver.

2 CORINTHIANS 9:6-7

Lord, hear my prayer today

_____

_____

_____

_____

_____

_____

_____

_____

_____

Refrain

Something I can do without today

_____

_____

_____

_____

_____

_____

_____

_____

_____

Give

Something I can give today

_____

_____

_____

_____

_____

_____

_____

_____

_____

Gratitude

Therefore, since we are receiving a kingdom that cannot be shaken, let us be thankful, and so worship God acceptably with reverence and awe, for our "God is a consuming fire."

HEBREWS 12:28

My prayer of thanksgiving

_____

_____

_____

_____

_____

_____

_____

_____

_____

_____

_____

"For I know the plans I have for you," declares
the Lord, *"plans to prosper you and not to
harm you, plans to give you hope and a future."*

JEREMIAH 29:11

My prayer for today

_____

_____

_____

_____

_____

_____

_____

_____

_____

Lord, help me reach my goals for today.

In my Easter journey, I determine what is unnecessary.

Today I am conscious of the following unnecessary demands on my time:

_____

_____

_____

_____

_____

May the gifting of the Spirit flow through me to illuminate all I come into contact with today.

What gifts am I consciously giving today?

_____

_____

_____

_____

_____

Set your minds on things above,
not on earthly things.

COLOSSIANS 3:2

Lord, hear my prayer today

_____

_____

_____

_____

_____

_____

_____

_____

_____

Refrain

Something I can do
without today

_____

_____

_____

_____

_____

_____

_____

_____

_____

Give

Something I can give
today

_____

_____

_____

_____

_____

_____

_____

_____

_____

Gratitude

The LORD is my strength and my shield; my heart trusts in him, and he helps me. My heart leaps for joy, and with my song I praise him.

PSALM 28:7

My prayer of thanksgiving

_____

_____

_____

_____

_____

_____

_____

_____

_____

_____

_____

Dear children, let us not love with words or speech but with actions and in truth.

1 JOHN 3:18

My prayer for today

_____

_____

_____

_____

_____

_____

_____

_____

_____

Lord, help me reach my goals for today.

In my Easter journey, I determine what is unnecessary.

Today I am conscious of the following unnecessary demands on my time:

_____

_____

_____

_____

_____

_____

May the gifting of the Spirit flow through me to illuminate all I come into contact with today.

What gifts am I consciously giving today?

_____

_____

_____

_____

_____

_____

Then he said to them all: "Whoever wants to be my disciple must deny themselves and take up their cross daily and follow me."

LUKE 9:23

Lord, my savior, hear my prayer today

_____

_____

_____

_____

_____

_____

_____

_____

_____

Refrain

Something I can do
without today

_____

_____

_____

_____

_____

_____

_____

_____

_____

_____

Give

Something I can give
today

_____

_____

_____

_____

_____

_____

_____

_____

_____

_____

Gratitude

Devote yourselves to prayer, being watchful and thankful.

COLOSSIANS 4:2

My prayer of thanksgiving

_____

_____

_____

_____

_____

_____

_____

_____

_____

_____

_____

In the same way, let your light shine before others, that they may see your good deeds and glorify your Father in heaven.

MATTHEW 5:16

My prayer for today

_____

_____

_____

_____

_____

_____

_____

_____

_____

Lord, help me reach my goals for today.

In my Easter journey, I determine what is unnecessary.

Today I am conscious of the following unnecessary demands on my time:

_____

_____

_____

_____

_____

May the gifting of the Spirit flow through me to illuminate all I come into contact with today.

What gifts am I consciously giving today?

_____

_____

_____

_____

_____

I can do all things through him who gives me strength.

PHILIPPIANS 4:13

Lord, my strength, hear my prayer today

_____

_____

_____

_____

_____

_____

_____

_____

_____

_____

Refrain

Something I can do
without today

_____

_____

_____

_____

_____

_____

_____

_____

_____

Give

Something I can give
today

_____

_____

_____

_____

_____

_____

_____

_____

_____

Gratitude

Enter his gates with thanksgiving and his courts with praise; give thanks to him and praise his name.
For the LORD is good and his love endures forever; his faithfulness continues through all generations.

PSALM 100:4-5

My prayer of thanksgiving

_____

_____

_____

_____

_____

_____

_____

_____

_____

_____

_____

For the wages of sin is death, but the gift of God is eternal life in Christ Jesus our Lord.

ROMANS 6:23

My prayer for today

_____

_____

_____

_____

_____

_____

_____

_____

_____

Lord, help me reach my goals for today.

In my Easter journey, I determine what is unnecessary.

Today I am conscious of the following unnecessary demands on my time:

_____

_____

_____

_____

_____

May the gifting of the Spirit flow through me to illuminate all I come into contact with today.

What gifts am I consciously giving today?

_____

_____

_____

_____

_____

He saved us, not because of righteous things we had done, but because of his mercy. He saved us through the washing of rebirth and renewal by the Holy Spirit.

Titus 3:5

Lord, my savior, hear my prayer today

_____

_____

_____

_____

_____

_____

_____

_____

_____

_____

Refrain

Something I can do without today

_____

_____

_____

_____

_____

_____

_____

_____

_____

Give

Something I can give today

_____

_____

_____

_____

_____

_____

_____

_____

Gratitude

Rejoice in the Lord always. I will say it again: Rejoice! Let your gentleness be evident to all. The Lord is near. Do not be anxious about anything, but in every situation, by prayer and petition, with thanksgiving, present your requests to God.

PHILIPPIANS 4:4-6

My prayer of thanksgiving

_____

_____

_____

_____

_____

_____

_____

_____

_____

_____

_____

_____

The Lord is my light and my salvation —
whom shall I fear?
The Lord is the stronghold of my life —
of whom shall I be afraid?

PSALM 27:1

My prayer for today

_____

_____

_____

_____

_____

_____

_____

_____

_____

Lord, help me reach my goals for today.

In my Easter journey, I determine what is unnecessary.

Today I am conscious of the following unnecessary demands on my time:

_____

_____

_____

_____

_____

May the gifting of the Spirit flow through me to illuminate all I come into contact with today.

What gifts am I consciously giving today?

_____

_____

_____

_____

_____

For Christ also suffered once for sins, the righteous for the unrighteous, to bring you to God. He was put to death in the body, but made alive in the Spirit.

1 PETER 3:18

Lord, my redeemer, hear my prayer today

_____

_____

_____

_____

_____

_____

_____

_____

_____

Refrain

Something I can do without today

_____

_____

_____

_____

_____

_____

_____

_____

_____

_____

Give

Something I can give today

_____

_____

_____

_____

_____

_____

_____

_____

_____

_____

Gratitude

Rejoice always, pray continually, give thanks in all circumstances; for this is God's will for you in Christ Jesus.

1 THESSALONIANS 5:16-18

My prayer of thanksgiving

_____

_____

_____

_____

_____

_____

_____

_____

_____

_____

_____

My prayer for today

_____

_____

_____

_____

_____

_____

_____

_____

_____

Lord, help me reach my goals for today.

In my Easter journey, I determine what is unnecessary.

Today I am conscious of the following unnecessary demands on my time:

_____

_____

_____

_____

_____

May the gifting of the Spirit flow through me to illuminate all I come into contact with today.

What gifts am I consciously giving today?

_____

_____

_____

_____

_____

I write these things to you who believe in the name of the Son of God so that you may know that you have eternal life.

1 JOHN 5:13

Lord, hear my prayer today

_____

_____

_____

_____

_____

_____

_____

_____

_____

_____

Refrain

Something I can do
without today

_____

_____

_____

_____

_____

_____

_____

_____

_____

Give

Something I can give
today

_____

_____

_____

_____

_____

_____

_____

_____

_____

Gratitude

Give thanks to the Lord, for he is good; his love endures forever.

PSALM 118:1

My prayer of thanksgiving

_____

_____

_____

_____

_____

_____

_____

_____

_____

_____

_____

And let us consider how we may spur one another on toward love and good deeds, not giving up meeting together, as some are in the habit of doing, but encouraging one another — and all the more as you see the day approaching.

HEBREWS 10:24-25

My prayer for today

_____

_____

_____

_____

_____

_____

_____

_____

_____

Lord, help me reach my goals for today.

In my Easter journey, I determine what is unnecessary.

Today I am conscious of the following unnecessary demands on my time:

_____

_____

_____

_____

_____

_____

May the gifting of the Spirit flow through me to illuminate all I come into contact with today.

What gifts am I consciously giving today?

_____

_____

_____

_____

_____

And my God will meet all your needs according to the riches of his glory in Christ Jesus.

PHILIPPIANS 4:19

Lord, my God, hear my prayer today

_____

_____

_____

_____

_____

_____

_____

_____

_____

Refrain

Something I can do
without today

_____

_____

_____

_____

_____

_____

_____

_____

_____

Give

Something I can give
today

_____

_____

_____

_____

_____

_____

_____

_____

_____

Gratitude

I will give thanks to you, Lord, with all my heart;
I will tell of all your wonderful deeds.
I will be glad and rejoice in you;
I will sing the praises of your name; Oh Most High.

PSALM 9:1-2

My prayer of thanksgiving

_____

_____

_____

_____

_____

_____

_____

_____

_____

_____

_____

"You have heard that it was said, 'Love your neighbor and hate your enemy.' But I tell you, love your enemies and pray for those who persecute you, that you may be children of your Father in heaven."

MATTHEW 5:43-45

My prayer for today

_____

_____

_____

_____

_____

_____

_____

_____

_____

_____

Lord, help me reach my goals for today.

In my Easter journey, I determine what is unnecessary.

Today I am conscious of the following unnecessary demands on my time:

_____

_____

_____

_____

_____

May the gifting of the Spirit flow through me to illuminate all I come into contact with today.

What gifts am I consciously giving today?

_____

_____

_____

_____

_____

But those who hope in the Lord will renew their strength.

They will soar on wings like eagles.

ISAIAH 40:31

Lord, my strength, hear my prayer today

_____

_____

_____

_____

_____

_____

_____

_____

_____

Refrain	Give
Something I can do without today	Something I can give today
_____	_____
_____	_____
_____	_____
_____	_____
_____	_____
_____	_____
_____	_____
_____	_____
_____	_____

Gratitude

Let the peace of Christ rule in your hearts, since as members of one body you were called to peace. And be thankful.

COLOSSIANS 3:15

My prayer of thanksgiving

"Everything is possible for one who believes."

MARK 9:23

My prayer for today

_____
_____
_____
_____
_____
_____
_____
_____
_____
_____

Lord, help me reach my goals for today.

In my Easter journey, I determine what is unnecessary.

Today I am conscious of the following unnecessary demands on my time:

_____

_____

_____

_____

_____

May the gifting of the Spirit flow through me to illuminate all I come into contact with today.

What gifts am I consciously giving today?

_____

_____

_____

_____

_____

I have been crucified with Christ and I no longer live, but Christ lives in me. The life I now live in the body, I live by faith in the Son of God, who loved me and gave himself for me.

GALATIANS 2:20

Lord, hear my prayer today

_____

_____

_____

_____

_____

_____

_____

_____

_____

Refrain	Give
Something I can do without today	Something I can give today

Gratitude

Give thanks to the Lord, for he is good; his love endures forever.

PSALM 107:1

My prayer of thanksgiving

I have told you these things, so that in me you may have peace. In this world you will have trouble. But take heart! I have overcome the world.

JOHN 16:33

My prayer for today

_____

_____

_____

_____

_____

_____

_____

_____

_____

Lord, help me reach my goals for today.

In my Easter journey, I determine what is unnecessary.

Today I am conscious of the following unnecessary demands on my time:

_____

_____

_____

_____

_____

May the gifting of the Spirit flow through me to illuminate all I come into contact with today.

What gifts am I consciously giving today?

_____

_____

_____

_____

_____

For we know, brothers and sisters loved by God, that he has chosen you, because our gospel came to you not simply with words but also with power, with the Holy Spirit and deep conviction.

1 THESSALONIANS 1:4-5

Lord, hear my prayer today

_____
_____
_____
_____
_____
_____
_____
_____
_____

Refrain

Something I can do without today

_____

_____

_____

_____

_____

_____

_____

_____

_____

Give

Something I can give today

_____

_____

_____

_____

_____

_____

_____

_____

_____

Gratitude

All this is for your benefit, so that the grace that is reaching more and more people may cause thanksgiving to overflow to the glory of God.

2 CORINTHIANS 4:15

My prayer of thanksgiving

_____

_____

_____

_____

_____

_____

_____

_____

_____

_____

_____

"I am the Lord, the God of all mankind. Is anything too hard for me?"

JEREMIAH 32:27

My prayer for today

_____

_____

_____

_____

_____

_____

_____

_____

_____

Lord, help me reach my goals for today.

In my Easter journey, I determine what is unnecessary.

Today I am conscious of the following unnecessary demands on my time:

_____

_____

_____

_____

_____

May the gifting of the Spirit flow through me to illuminate all I come into contact with today.

What gifts am I consciously giving today?

_____

_____

_____

_____

_____

So I strive always to keep my conscience clear before God and man.

ACTS 24:16

Lord, hear my prayer today

_____
_____
_____
_____
_____
_____
_____
_____
_____

Refrain

Something I can do
without today

_____

_____

_____

_____

_____

_____

_____

_____

_____

_____

Give

Something I can give
today

_____

_____

_____

_____

_____

_____

_____

_____

_____

_____

Gratitude

Sing and make music from your heart to the Lord, always giving thanks to God the Father for everything, in the name of our Lord Jesus Christ.

EPHESIANS 5:19-20

My prayer of thanksgiving

_____

_____

_____

_____

_____

_____

_____

_____

_____

_____

_____

We all, like sheep, have gone astray, each of us has turned to our own way; and the Lord has laid on him the iniquity of us all.

ISAIAH 53:6

My prayer for today

_____

_____

_____

_____

_____

_____

_____

_____

_____

Lord, help me reach my goals for today.

In my Easter journey, I determine what is unnecessary.

Today I am conscious of the following unnecessary demands on my time:

_____

_____

_____

_____

_____

May the gifting of the Spirit flow through me to illuminate all I come into contact with today.

What gifts am I consciously giving today?

_____

_____

_____

_____

_____

Consider him who endured such opposition from sinners, so that you will not grow weary and lose heart.

HEBREWS 12:3

Lord, hear my prayer today

_____

_____

_____

_____

_____

_____

_____

_____

_____

_____

Refrain

Something I can do
without today

_____

_____

_____

_____

_____

_____

_____

_____

_____

Give

Something I can give
today

_____

_____

_____

_____

_____

_____

_____

_____

_____

Gratitude

From them will come songs of thanksgiving and the sound of rejoicing.

I will add to their numbers, and they will not be decreased.

JEREMIAH 30:19

My prayer of thanksgiving

_____

_____

_____

_____

_____

_____

_____

_____

_____

_____

_____

But seek first his kingdom and his righteousness, and all these things will be given to you as well.

MATTHEW 6:33

My prayer for today

_____

_____

_____

_____

_____

_____

_____

_____

_____

_____

Lord, help me reach my goals for today.

In my Easter journey, I determine what is unnecessary.

Today I am conscious of the following unnecessary demands on my time:

_____

_____

_____

_____

_____

May the gifting of the Spirit flow through me to illuminate all I come into contact with today.

What gifts am I consciously giving today?

_____

_____

_____

_____

_____

For even the Son of Man did not come to be served, but to serve, and to give his life as a ransom for many.

MARK 10:45

Lord, hear my prayer today

_____

_____

_____

_____

_____

_____

_____

_____

_____

Refrain

Something I can do
without today

_____

_____

_____

_____

_____

_____

_____

_____

_____

_____

Give

Something I can give
today

_____

_____

_____

_____

_____

_____

_____

_____

_____

_____

Gratitude

And whatever you do, whether in word or deed, do it all in the name of the Lord Jesus, giving thanks to God the Father through him.

COLOSSIANS 3:17

My prayer of thanksgiving

_____

_____

_____

_____

_____

_____

_____

_____

_____

_____

_____

_____

Therefore, my dear brothers and sisters, stand firm. Let nothing move you. Always give yourselves fully to the work of the Lord, because you know that your labor in the Lord is not in vain.

1 CORINTHIANS 15:58

My prayer for today

_____

_____

_____

_____

_____

_____

_____

_____

_____

Lord, help me reach my goals for today.

In my Easter journey, I determine what is unnecessary.

Today I am conscious of the following unnecessary demands on my time:

_____

_____

_____

_____

_____

May the gifting of the Spirit flow through me to illuminate all I come into contact with today.

What gifts am I consciously giving today?

_____

_____

_____

_____

_____

Very truly I tell you, whoever hears my word and believes in him who sent me has eternal life and will not be judged but has crossed over from death to life.

JOHN 5:24

Lord, hear my prayer today

_____

_____

_____

_____

_____

_____

_____

_____

_____

Refrain

Something I can do without today

_____

_____

_____

_____

_____

_____

_____

_____

_____

_____

Give

Something I can give today

_____

_____

_____

_____

_____

_____

_____

_____

_____

_____

Gratitude

*Let them give thanks to the Lord for his unfailing love
and his wonderful deeds for mankind,
for he satisfies the thirsty
and fills the hungry with good things.*

PSALM 107:8-9

My prayer of thanksgiving

_____

_____

_____

_____

_____

_____

_____

_____

_____

_____

_____

Do not conform to the pattern of this world, but be transformed by the renewing of your mind.

ROMANS 12:2

My prayer for today

_____
_____
_____
_____
_____
_____
_____
_____
_____

Lord, help me reach my goals for today.

In my Easter journey, I determine what is unnecessary.

Today I am conscious of the following unnecessary demands on my time:

_____

_____

_____

_____

_____

_____

May the gifting of the Spirit flow through me to illuminate all I come into contact with today.

What gifts am I consciously giving today?

_____

_____

_____

_____

_____

_____

Because of the Lord's great love we are not consumed, for his compassions never fail. They are new every morning; great is your faithfulness.

LAMENTATIONS 3:22-23

Lord, hear my prayer today

_____
_____
_____
_____
_____
_____
_____
_____
_____
_____

Refrain

Something I can do without today

_____

_____

_____

_____

_____

_____

_____

_____

_____

Give

Something I can give today

_____

_____

_____

_____

_____

_____

_____

_____

_____

Gratitude

Now, our God, we give you thanks,
and praise your glorious name.

1 CHRONICLES 29:13

My prayer of thanksgiving

For it is by grace you have been saved, through faith — and this not from yourselves, it is the gift of God.

EPHESIANS 2:8

My prayer for today

_____

_____

_____

_____

_____

_____

_____

_____

_____

Lord, help me reach my goals for today.

In my Easter journey, I determine what is unnecessary.

Today I am conscious of the following unnecessary demands on my time:

_____

_____

_____

_____

_____

May the gifting of the Spirit flow through me to illuminate all I come into contact with today.

What gifts am I consciously giving today?

_____

_____

_____

_____

_____

"Truly, I tell you, today you will be with me in paradise."

LUKE 23:43

Lord, hear my prayer today

_____

_____

_____

_____

_____

_____

_____

_____

_____

Refrain

Something I can do
without today

_____

_____

_____

_____

_____

_____

_____

_____

_____

Give

Something I can give
today

_____

_____

_____

_____

_____

_____

_____

_____

_____

Gratitude

I will praise God's name in song and glorify him with thanksgiving.

PSALM 69:30

My prayer of thanksgiving

_____

_____

_____

_____

_____

_____

_____

_____

_____

_____

_____

_____

What we have received is not the spirit of the world, but the Spirit who is from God, so that we may understand what God has freely given us.

1 CORINTHIANS 2:12

My prayer for today

_____

_____

_____

_____

_____

_____

_____

_____

_____

Lord, help me reach my goals for today.

In my Easter journey, I determine what
is unnecessary.

Today I am conscious of the following
unnecessary demands on my time:

_____

_____

_____

_____

_____

May the gifting of the Spirit flow through
me to illuminate all I come into contact
with today.

What gifts am I consciously giving today?

_____

_____

_____

_____

_____

But God demonstrates his own love for us in this:
While we were still sinners, Christ died for us.

ROMANS 5:8

Lord, hear my prayer today

_____

_____

_____

_____

_____

_____

_____

_____

_____

Refrain

Something I can do
without today

_____

_____

_____

_____

_____

_____

_____

_____

_____

_____

Give

Something I can give
today

_____

_____

_____

_____

_____

_____

_____

_____

_____

_____

Gratitude

Come, let us sing for the joy of the Lord;
    let us shout aloud to the Rock of our salvation.
Let us come before him with thanksgiving
    and extol him with music and song.

PSALM 95:1-2

My prayer of thanksgiving

_____

_____

_____

_____

_____

_____

_____

_____

_____

_____

_____